# 4-Chord Songbook
## The Beatles

**WISE PUBLICATIONS**
**part of The Music Sales Group**
London / New York / Paris / Sydney / Copenhagen / Berlin / Madrid / Tokyo

Published by
Wise Publications
14-15 Berners Street, London W1T 3LJ, UK.

Exclusive Distributors:
Music Sales Limited
Distribution Centre, Newmarket Road, Bury St Edmunds, Suffolk IP33 3YB, UK.
Music Sales Pty Limited
120 Rothschild Avenue, Rosebery, NSW 2018, Australia.

Order No. NO91135
ISBN 1-84609-841-6
This book © Copyright 2006 Wise Publications,
a division of Music Sales Limited.

Printed in the EU.

www.musicsales.com

Your Guarantee of Quality

As publishers, we strive to produce every book to the highest commercial standards.

The music has been freshly engraved and the book has been carefully designed to minimise
awkward page turns and to make playing from it a real pleasure.

Particular care has been given to specifying acid-free, neutral-sized paper made
from pulps which have not been elemental chlorine bleached.

This pulp is from farmed sustainable forests and was produced with special regard for the environment.

Throughout, the printing and binding have been planned to ensure a sturdy,
attractive publication which should give years of enjoyment.

If your copy fails to meet our high standards, please inform us and we will gladly replace it.

**All Together Now**
page 8

**The Ballad Of John And Yoko**
page 5

**Drive My Car**
page 10

**Eleanor Rigby**
page 12

**Get Back**
page 14

**Hello Goodbye**
page 16

**If You've Got Trouble**
page 18

**I'm Down**
page 20

**I've Just Seen A Face**
page 22

**Let It Be**
page 24

**Love Me Do**
page 26

**Misery**
page 28

**Ob-La-Di, Ob-La-Da**
page 30

**Octopus's Garden**
page 32

**Paperback Writer**
page 34

**Rain**
page 36

**Taxman**
page 38

**Tell Me What You See**
page 40

**Thank You Girl**
page 42

**Twist And Shout**
page 44

**Yellow Submarine**
page 46

This *4-Chord Songbook* allows even beginner guitarists to play and enjoy classic hits. With the same 4 chords used throughout the book, you'll soon master your favourite Beatles songs.

The *4-Chord Songbook* doesn't use music notation. Throughout the book chord boxes are printed at the head of each song; the chord changes are shown above the lyrics. It's left to you, the guitarist, to decide on a strum pattern or picking pattern.

You might find that the pitch of the vocal line is not always comfortable because it is pitched too high or too low. In that case, you can change the key without learning a new set of chords; simply place a capo behind a suitable fret.

Whatever you do, this *4-Chord Songbook* guarantees hours of enjoyment for guitarists of all levels, as well as providing a fine basis for building a strong repertoire.

# The Ballad Of John And Yoko

Words & Music by
John Lennon & Paul McCartney

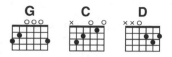

**Intro**    | G    | G    ||

**Verse 1**

**G**
Standing in the dock at Southampton,

Trying to get to Holland or France.

The man in the mac said,

"You've got to go back,"

You know they didn't give us a chance.

**Chorus 1**

Christ! You know it ain't easy,  **C**

You know how hard it can be.  **G**

The way things are going,  **D**

They're gonna crucify me.  **G**

**Verse 2**

**G**
Finally made the plane into Paris,

Honeymooning down by the Seine.

Peter Brown called to say,

"You can make it OK,

You can get married in Gibraltar, near Spain."

| | |
|---|---|
| *Chorus 2* | As Chorus 1 |

*Verse 3*

**G**
Drove from Paris to the Amsterdam Hilton,

Talking in our beds for a week.

The newspeople said,

"Say what you doing in bed?"

I said, "We're only trying to get us some peace."

| | |
|---|---|
| *Chorus 3* | As Chorus 1 |

*Bridge*

**C**
Saving up your money for a rainy day,

Giving all your clothes to charity.

Last night the wife said,

"Oh boy when you're dead,

   **D**
You don't take nothing with you but your soul."

Think!

*Verse 4*

**G**
Made a lightning trip to Vienna,

Eating chocolate cake in a bag.

The newspapers said,

"She's gone to his head,

They look just like two gurus in drag."

|            |                                         |
|------------|-----------------------------------------|
|            | **C**                                   |
| *Chorus 4* | Christ! You know it ain't easy,         |
|            | **G**                                   |
|            | You know how hard it can be.            |
|            | **D**                                   |
|            | The way things are going,               |
|            | **G**                                   |
|            | They're gonna crucify me.               |

|           |                                              |
|-----------|----------------------------------------------|
|           | **G**                                        |
| *Verse 5* | Caught the early plane back to London,       |
|           | Fifty acorns tied in a sack.                 |
|           | The men from the press said,                 |
|           | "We wish you success,                        |
|           | It's good to have the both of you back."     |

|            |                                         |
|------------|-----------------------------------------|
|            | **C**                                   |
| *Chorus 5* | Christ! You know it ain't easy,         |
|            | **G**                                   |
|            | You know how hard it can be.            |
|            | **D**                                   |
|            | The way things are going,               |
|            | **G**                                   |
|            | They're gonna crucify me.               |

|          |                                    |
|----------|------------------------------------|
|          | **D**                              |
| *Coda*   | The way things are going,          |
|          | **G**                              |
|          | They're gonna crucify me.          |

| D | D | G | G ‖

# All Together Now

Words & Music by
John Lennon & Paul McCartney

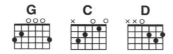

**Intro**  ‖: G  |  G  |  G  |  G   :‖

**Verse 1**

**G**                     **D**
One, two, three, four, can I have a little more?
**G**                   **D**        **G**
Five, six, seven, eight, nine, ten, I love you.

**Verse 2**

**G**       **D**
A, B, C, D, can I bring my friend to tea?
**G**           **D**      **G**
E, F, G, H, I, J, I love you.

**Bridge 1**

(Boom boom boom
**C**
Boom boom boom.) Sail the ship,
**G**
(Boom boom boom.) Chop the tree,
**C**
(Boom boom boom.) Skip the rope,
**D**
(Boom boom boom.) Look at me! _____

(All together now.)

**Chorus 1**

**G**
All together now, (all together now.)

All together now, (all together now.)
**D**
All together now, (all together now.)
**G**
All together now, (all together now.)

|                | **G**                                        **D** |
|----------------|---------------------------------------------|
| *Verse 3*      | Black, white, green, red, can I take my friend to bed? |

*Verse 3*

**G**         **D**

Black, white, green, red, can I take my friend to bed?

**G**           **D**    **G**

Pink, brown, yellow, orange and blue, I love you.

(All together now.)

*Chorus 2*

‖: **G**

All together now, (all together now.)

All together now, (all together now.)

**D**

All together now, (all together now.)

**G**

All together now, (all together now.)   :‖

*Bridge 2*

(Boom boom boom

**C**

Boom boom boom.) Sail the ship,

**G**

(Boom boom boom.) Chop the tree,

**C**

(Boom boom boom.) Skip the rope,

**D**

(Boom boom boom.) Look at me! ____

(All together now.)

*Chorus 3*

‖: **G**

All together now, (all together now.)

All together now, (all together now.)

**D**

All together now, (all together now.)

**G**

All together now, (all together now.)   :‖

*Chorus 4*

**G**

All together now, (all together now.)

All together now, (all together now.)

**D**

All together now, (all together now.)

      **G**

All together now. ____

# Drive My Car

Words & Music by
John Lennon & Paul McCartney

G    C    D    Em

*(2 bar count in)*

**Intro**      | (G)      | (G)        ||

           G                    C

**Verse 1**    Asked a girl what she wanted to be,

           G         C

She said, "Baby, can't you see?

           G         C

I wanna be famous, a star of the screen,

             D

But you can do something in between."

       Em                  C  Em         C

**Chorus 1**  Baby, you can drive my car, yes I'm gonna be a star,

       Em              C    D    G     C D

Baby, you can drive my car, and maybe I'll love you.

           G                    C

**Verse 2**    I told that girl that my prospects were good,

           G           C

She said, "Baby, it's understood.

           G         C

Working for peanuts is all very fine,

             D

But I can show you a better time."

       Em                  C  Em         C

**Chorus 2**  Baby, you can drive my car, yes I'm gonna be a star,

       Em              C    D    G     C

Baby, you can drive my car, and maybe I'll love you.

           N.C.

Beep beep mm beep beep, yeah!

*Guitar solo*    | G      | G      | G      | G      |

                   | C      | C      | D      | D      ||

*Chorus 3*

Em                         C    Em                C
Baby, you can drive my car, yes I'm gonna be a star,
Em                        C     D      G     C D
Baby, you can drive my car, and maybe I'll love you.

*Verse 3*

G                      C
   I told that girl I could start right away,
G                             C
   And she said, "Listen, babe, I've got something to say,
G                  C
   I've got no car, and it's breaking my heart,
     D
But I've found a driver, and that's a start."

*Chorus 4*

Em                         C    Em                C
Baby, you can drive my car, yes I'm gonna be a star,
Em                        C     D      G     C
Baby, you can drive my car, and maybe I'll love you.
D  N.C.                     G    C
   Beep beep mm beep beep, yeah!
    D                        G  C
‖:   Beep beep mm beep beep, yeah!    :‖ *Play 6 times to fade*

# Eleanor Rigby

Words & Music by
John Lennon & Paul McCartney

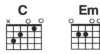

**Intro**

C        Em
Ah, look at all the lonely people!
C        Em
Ah, look at all the lonely people!

**Verse 1**

Em
Eleanor Rigby,

                    C
Picks up the rice in the church where a wedding has been,
       Em
Lives in a dream. _____

Waits at the window,

               Em  C
Wearing a face that she keeps in a jar by the door,
     Em
Who is it for?

**Chorus 1**

Em
All the lonely people, where do they all come from?
Em
All the lonely people, where do they all belong?

**Verse 2**

Em
Father McKenzie,

                 C
Writing the words of a sermon that no-one will hear,
       Em
No-one comes near.

Look at him working,

                   C
Darning his socks in the night when there's nobody there,
      Em
What does he care?

*Chorus 2*

**Em**
All the lonely people, where do they all come from?

**Em**
All the lonely people, where do they all belong?


*Bridge*

**C**                         **Em**
Ah, look at all the lonely people!

**C**                         **Em**
Ah, look at all the lonely people!


*Verse 3*

**Em**
Eleanor Rigby

                                                    **C**
Died in the church and was buried along with her name,

          **Em**
Nobody came.

Father McKenzie,

                                                    **C**
Wiping the dirt from his hands as he walks from the grave,

          **Em**
No-one was saved.


*Chorus 3*

**Em**
All the lonely people, where do they all come from?

**Em**
All the lonely people, where do they all belong?

# Get Back

Words & Music by
John Lennon & Paul McCartney

G     C     D

***Intro***    | D  | D  | D  | D  C  G  ||

***Verse 1***

D
Jojo was a man who thought he was a loner
G                  D
But he knew it couldn't last.

Jojo left his home in Tucson, Arizona
G               D
For some California grass.

***Chorus 1***

D
Get back, get back,
G               D     C  G
Get back to where you once belonged.
D
Get back, get back,
G               D
Get back to where you once belonged.

Get back Jojo.

***Solo***    ||: (D)  | D  | G  | D  C  G :||

***Chorus 2***

D
Get back, get back,
G               D     C  G
Get back to where you once belonged.
D
Get back, get back,
D               G
Get back to where you once belonged.
D
Get back Jo.

*Solo*  ‖: (D)    | D    | G    | D   C  G :‖

*Verse 2*

**D**
Sweet Loretta Martin thought she was a woman
**G**           **D**
But she was another man.

All the girls around her say she's got it coming
**G**               **D**
But she gets it while she can.

*Chorus 3*

           **D**
Get back, get back,
        **G**                    **D**      **C  G**
Get back to where you once belonged.
           **D**
Get back, get back,
        **G**                    **D**
Get back to where you once belonged.

Get back Loretta.

*Solo*  ‖: D    | D    | G    | D   C  G :‖

*Chorus 4*

           **D**
Get back, get back,
        **G**                    **D**      **C  G**
Get back to where you once belonged.
           **D**
Get back, get back,
        **G**
Get back to where you once belonged.   Ooh.

‖: D    | D    | G    | D   C  G :‖  *Repeat to fade*
        Get back.

# Hello Goodbye

Words & Music by
John Lennon & Paul McCartney

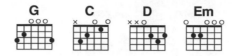

**Verse 1**

   C             G
You say yes, I say no,

   D               Em          D
You stay stop, but I say go, go, go.

   Em   D
  Oh no.

                               C
You say goodbye and I say;

**Chorus 1**

   G             Em
Hello,    hello, hello,

                    C
I don't know why you say goodbye, I say hello,

   G             Em
Hello,    hello, hello,

                   C          D        G
I don't know why you say goodbye, I say hello.

**Verse 2**

   C            G
I say high, you say low,

   D               Em          D
You say why and I say I don't know.

   Em   D
  Oh no.

                               C
You say goodbye and I say hello.

*Chorus 2*

      G                          Em
{ (Hello, goodbye, hello, goodbye,)
                        Hello, hello,

                         C                                 G
{ (Hello, goodbye.)      I don't know why you say goodbye, I say hello.

                                 Em
{ (Hello, goodbye, hello, goodbye,)
                        Hello, hello,

                         C              D          G
{ (Hello, goodbye,)     I don't know why you say goodbye, I say hello.
                                    (Hello, goodbye.)

*Link*

    C  G            D
      Why, why, why, why, why, why,
        Em           D
Do you say goodbye, goodbye?
 Em    D
  Oh no.
D                 C
You say goodbye and I say;

*Chorus 3*     As Chorus 1

*Verse 3*

 C          G
{ You say yes,  I say no,
          (I say yes, but I may mean no,)
 D                  Em        D
{ You say stop,       but I say go, go, go.
        (I can stay till it's time to go)
  Em   D
    Oh, no.
D                 C
You say goodbye and I say;

*Chorus 4*     As Chorus 1

*Chorus 5*

G          Em
  Hello, hello,
            C
I don't know why you say goodbye, I say hello, _____
   G
Hello.

*Coda*      G
      ‖: Hela, heba, helloa. :‖  *Repeat to fade*

# If You've Got Trouble

Words & Music by
John Lennon & Paul McCartney

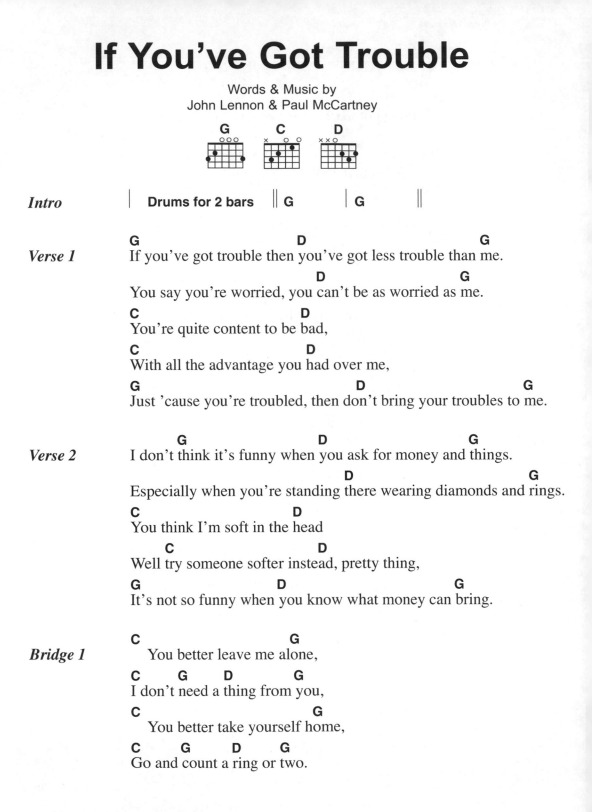

**Intro**

| Drums for 2 bars ‖ G | G ‖

**Verse 1**

G              D             G
If you've got trouble then you've got less trouble than me.

                    D         G
You say you're worried, you can't be as worried as me.

C            D
You're quite content to be bad,

C            D
With all the advantage you had over me,

G              D            G
Just 'cause you're troubled, then don't bring your troubles to me.

**Verse 2**

G             D            G
I don't think it's funny when you ask for money and things.

                   D         G
Especially when you're standing there wearing diamonds and rings.

C            D
You think I'm soft in the head

       C            D
Well try someone softer instead, pretty thing,

G            D            G
It's not so funny when you know what money can bring.

**Bridge 1**

C            G
    You better leave me alone,

C   G   D   G
I don't need a thing from you,

C            G
    You better take yourself home,

C   G   D   G
Go and count a ring or two.

*Verse 3*

```
G                           D                        G
If you've got trouble then you've got less trouble than me.
                              D                    G
You say you're worried, you can't be as worried as me.
C                   D
You're quite content to be bad,
C                           D
With all the advantage you had over me,
G                           D                            G
Just 'cause you're troubled, then don't bring your troubles to me.
```

(Oh rock on, anybody!)

*Solo*

```
| G      | G      | G      | G      | C      | C      |
| G      | G      | D      | C      | G      | G      ||
```

*Bridge 2*

```
C                 G
  You better leave me alone,
C     G    D     G
I don't need a thing from you,
C                       G
  You better take yourself home,
C     G     D     G
Go and count a ring or two.
```

*Verse 4*

```
G                           D                        G
If you've got trouble then you've got less trouble than me.
                              D                    G
You say you're worried, you can't be as worried as me.
C                   D
You're quite content to be bad,
C                           D
With all the advantage you had over me,
G                           D                            G
Just 'cause you're troubled, then don't bring your troubles to me,
                              D                    G
Just 'cause you're troubled, then don't bring your troubles to me.
```

# I'm Down

Words & Music by
John Lennon & Paul McCartney

G      C      D

**Verse 1**

N.C.
You tell lies thinkin' I can't see,

G    N.C.
You can't cry 'cause you're laughing at me.

**Chorus 1**

C
I'm down, (I'm really down,)

G
I'm down, (down on the ground,)

C
I'm down, (I'm really down,)

D          G      N.C.
How can you laugh when you know I'm down?

D          G      N.C.
(How can you laugh) when you know I'm down?

**Verse 2**

G    N.C.
Man buys ring, woman throws it away,

G    N.C.
Same old thing happen every day.

**Chorus 2**

C
I'm down, (I'm really down,)

G
I'm down, (down on the ground,)

C
I'm down, (I'm really down,)

D          G      N.C.
How can you laugh when you know I'm down?

D          G      N.C.
(How can you laugh) when you know I'm down?

**Solo**

| (G)  | (G)  | (G)  | (G)  | C  | C  |

*Guitar*

| G  | G  | D  | D  | G  | G  ‖

*Verse 3*

G    N.C.
We're all alone and there's nobody else,

G    N.C.
You still moan, keep your hands to yourself.

*Chorus 3*

      C
I'm down, (I'm really down,)

      G
I'm down, (down on the ground,)

      C
I'm down, (I'm really down,)

D       G   N.C.
How can you laugh when you know I'm down?

D       G   N.C.
(How can you laugh) when you know I'm down?

*Solo 2*

| G | G | G | G | C | C |

*Keyboard*

| G | G | D | C | G | D |

*Coda*

                   G
‖: Oh babe, you know I'm down, (I'm really down,)

Oh yes I'm down, (I'm really down,)

            C
I'm down on the ground, (I'm really down,)

    G
I'm down, (I'm really down,)

            D    C
Ah, baby, I'm upside  down.

         G       D
Oh yeah, yeah, yeah, yeah, yeah. :‖ *Repeat ad lib. to fade*

# I've Just Seen A Face

Words & Music by
John Lennon & Paul McCartney

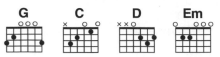

**Intro**   | Em | Em | Em | Em | C |

| C | C | C | D | D ||

**Verse 1**

G
I've just seen a face,

                                               Em
I can't forget the time or place where we just met,

She's just the girl for me

                           Em       C
And I want all the world to see we've met.

                D          G
Mm mm mm mm-mm mm.

**Verse 2**

G
Had it been another day

I might have looked the other way

      Em
And I'd have never been aware,

                        Em   C
But as it is I'll dream of her  tonight,

        D      G
Da da da da-da da.

**Chorus 1**

D               C
Falling, yes I am falling,

                  G     C        G
And she keeps calling   me back again.

*Verse 3*

       **G**
I have never know the like of this,

I've been alone and I have
**Em**
Missed things and kept out of sight,

                               **C**
But other girls were never quite like this,
       **D**      **G**
Da da da da-da da.

*Chorus 2*     As Chorus 1

*Solo*       | G    | G    | G    | G    | Em   | Em   |

               | Em  | Em     | C    | C    | D   | G   ||

               **D**           **C**
*Chorus 3*  Falling, yes I am falling,
                        **G**    **C**      **G**
              And she keeps calling  me back again.

               **G**
*Verse 4*   I've just seen a face,

                                                         **Em**
I can't forget the time or place where we just met,

She's just the girl for me

                                     **C**
And I want all the world to see we've met.
           **D**      **G**
Mm mm mm, da-da da.

*Chorus 4*  As Chorus 1

*Chorus 5*  As Chorus 1

               **D**          **C**
*Coda*      Oh, falling, yes I am falling,
                      **G**    **C**           **D** **G**
And she keeps calling  me back again.

# Let It Be

Words & Music by
John Lennon & Paul McCartney

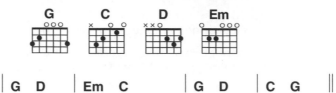

**Intro**    | G   D  | Em   C        | G   D  | C   G   ||

**Verse 1**

               **G**                **D**
When I find myself in times of trouble,
**Em**        **C**
Mother Mary comes to me,
**G**                 **D**            **C   G**
Speaking words of wisdom, let it be.
       **G**            **D**
And in my hour of darkness
          **Em**          **C**
She is standing right in front of me,
**G**                 **G**         **C   G**
Speaking words of wisdom, let it be.

**Chorus 1**

           **Em**   **G**    **C**     **G**
Let it be, let it be, let it be, let it be,
                    **D**         **C   G**
Whisper words of wisdom, let it be.

**Verse 2**

         **G**              **D**
And when the broken hearted people
**Em**        **C**
Living in the world agree,
**G**                 **D**          **C   G**
There will be an answer, let it be.
       **G**              **D**
For though they may be parted there is
**Em**           **C**
Still a chance that they will see.
**G**                 **D**          **C   G**
There will be an answer, let it be.

     **Em**    **G**    **C**    **G**
Let it be, let it be, let it be, let it be,
               **D**    **C G**
There will be an answer, let it be.
     **Em**    **G**    **C**    **G**
Let it be, let it be, let it be, let it be,
               **D**    **C G**
Whisper words of wisdom, let it be.

| C  G | D C G | C  G | D C G |

*Solo*    ‖: G  D | Em  C | G  D | C  G :‖

*Chorus 3*

     **Em**    **G**    **C**    **G**
Let it be, let it be, let it be, let it be,
               **D**    **C G**
Whisper words of wisdom, let it be.

*Verse 3*

    **G**             **D**
And when the night is cloudy,
       **Em**       **C**
There is still a light that shines on me,
**G**       **D**       **C G**
Shine until tomorrow, let it be.
    **F**       **D**
I wake up to the sound of music,
**Em**     **C**
Mother Mary comes to me,
**G**       **D**     **C G**
Speaking words of wisdom, let it be.

*Chorus 4*

     **Em**    **G**    **C**    **G**
Let it be, let it be, let it be, let it be,
               **D**    **C G**
There will be an answer, let it be.
     **Em**    **G**    **C**    **G**
Let it be, let it be, let it be, let it be,
               **D**    **C G**
There will be an answer, let it be.
     **Em**    **G**    **C**    **G**
Let it be, let it be, let it be, let it be,
               **D**    **C G**
Whisper words of wisdom, let it be.

| C  G | D C G ‖

# Love Me Do

Words & Music by
John Lennon & Paul McCartney

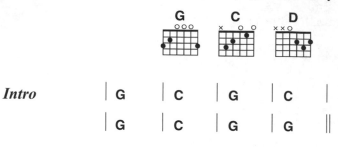

**Intro**

| G | C | G | C |

| G | C | G | G ||

**Chorus 1**

G　　　　　　　C
Love, love me do,
　　G　　　　　　C
You know I love you.
　　G　　　　　C
I'll always be true,

So please ____
N.C.　　　G　　C　G　　　　　C
Love me do, __ oh, love me do.

**Chorus 2**

G　　　　　　　C
Love, love me do,
　　G　　　　　　C
You know I love you.
　　G　　　　　C
I'll always be true,

So please ____
N.C.　　　G　　C　G　　　　　C
Love me do, __ oh, love me do.

**Bridge**

D
Someone to love,
C　　　　　G
Somebody new.
D
Someone to love,
C　　　　　　G
Someone like you.

*Chorus 3*
G                 C
Love, love me do,

     G            C
You know I love you.

     G            C
I'll always be true,

So please ____

**N.C.**      G     C     G
Love me do, ___ oh, love me do.

*Solo*       ‖: D     | D     | C     | G     :‖

            | G     | G     | G     | G  (D)  ‖

*Chorus 4*
G                 C
Love, love me do,

     G            C
You know I love you.

     G            C
I'll always be true,

So please ____

**N.C.**      G     C     G         C
Love me do, ___ oh, love me do.

              G         C
‖: Yeah, love me do,

           G          C
Oh, love me do.  :‖  *Repeat to fade*

# Misery

Words & Music by
John Lennon & Paul McCartney

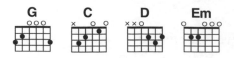

**Intro**

C                               **D**
The world is treating me bad, ___

**G**       **Em D**
Misery.

**Verse 1**

**G**            **C**
I'm the kind of guy

      **G**          **C**
Who never used to cry,

                        **D**
The world is treating me bad, ___

**G**       **Em**
Misery.

**Verse 2**

       **G**        **C**
I've lost her now for sure,

     **G**          **C**
I won't see her no more,

               **D**
It's gonna be a drag, ___

**G**
Misery.

**Bridge 1**

**Em**                        **G**
I'll remember all the little things we've done,

**Em**                         **D**
Can't she see she'll always be the only one,

Only one.

*Verse 3*

G                  C
Send her back to me,

        G          C
'Cause everyone can see,

                    D
Without her I will be ____

  G
In misery.

*Bridge 2*

Em                             G
I'll remember all the little things we've done,

Em                                     D
She'll remember and she'll miss her only one,

Lonely one.

*Verse 4*

G                  C
Send her back to me,

        G          C
'Cause everyone can see,

                    D
Without her I will be ____

  G
In misery,

Em    G      Em
Oh, in misery, ooh, ____

        G
My misery,

Em                G
La, la, la, la, la, la, misery.

# Ob-La-Di, Ob-La-Da

Words & Music by
John Lennon & Paul McCartney

G    C    D    Em

*Intro*     | G   | G   | G   | G    ||

*Verse 1*

```
     G                                    D
Desmond has a barrow in the market place,
                         G
Molly is a singer in a band.
                                   C
Desmond says to Molly, girl, I like your face,
                 G              D               G
And Molly says this as she takes him by the hand.
```

*Chorus 1*

```
              G                D   Em
Ob-La-Di, Ob-La-Da, life goes on, bra,
G          D      G
La-la how their life goes on.
              G                D   Em
Ob-La-Di, Ob-La-Da, life goes on, bra,
G          D      G
La-la how their life goes on.
```

*Verse 2*

```
     G                             D
Desmond takes a trolley to the jeweller's store,
D                       G
Buys a twenty carat golden ring.
                              C
Takes it back to Molly waiting at the door,
              G            D           G
And as he gives it to her, she begins to sing:
```

*Chorus 2*     As Chorus 1

*Middle 1*  
       **C**  
    In a couple of years,

                                **G**  
They have built a home sweet home.  
**C**  
  With a couple of kids running in the yard  
  **G**               **D**  
Of Desmond and Molly Jones.

*Verse 3*  
**G**                **D**  
Happy ever after in the market place,  
                         **G**  
Desmond lets the children lend a hand.  
                           **C**  
Molly stays at home and does her pretty face,  
        **G**         **D**       **G**  
And in the evening she still sings it with the band.

*Chorus 3*     As Chorus 1

*Middle 2*     As Middle 1

*Verse 4*  
**G**                **D**  
Happy ever after in the market place,  
**D**                   **G**  
Molly lets the children lend a hand.  
                          **C**  
Desmond stays at home and does his pretty face,  
      **A**        **D**       **G**  
And in the evening she's a singer with the band.

*Chorus 4*  
        **G**                  **D**  **Em**  
Ob-La-Di, Ob-La-Da, life goes on, bra,  
**G**           **D**     **G**  
La-la how their life goes on.  
        **G**                  **D**  **Em**  
Ob-La-Di, Ob-La-Da, life goes on, bra,  
**G**           **D**     **Em**  
La-la how their life goes on,

And if you want some fun,  
     **D**       **G**  
Take Ob-La-Di-Bla-Da.

# Octopus's Garden

Words & Music by
Ringo Starr

G  C  D  Em

**Intro**  | (G)  (D) | (G)  ‖ G  | Em  | C  | D  ‖

**Verse 1**

G           Em
I'd like to be   under the sea,

     C                      D
In an octopus's garden in the shade.

G           Em
He'd let us in,   knows where we've been,

      C                       D
In his octopus's garden in the shade.

Em
I'd ask my friends to come and see

C             D
An octopus's garden with me.

**Chorus 1**

G           Em
I'd like to be   under the sea

     C     D          G
In an octopus's garden in the shade.

**Verse 2**

G                Em
We would be warm   below the storm

      C                     D
In our little hideaway beneath the waves.

G            Em
Resting our head   on the sea bed

      C                 D
In an octopus's garden near a cave.

*cont.*

      **Em**
      We would sing and dance around,
  **C**                    **D**
  Because we know we can't be found.

*Chorus 2*

  **G**         **Em**
      I'd like to be   under the sea
        **C**       **D**        **G**
In an octopus's garden in the shade.

*Solo*

| C | | | | G | |
|---|---|---|---|---|---|

Ah,  ah,   ah.      Ah,  ah,   ah.

| C | | | G | C D | ‖
|---|---|---|---|---|---|

Ah,  ah,   ah.      Ah, ——  ah. ——

*Verse 3*

  **G**              **Em**
      We would shout   and swim about
       **C**                  **D**
The coral that lies beneath the waves.
  **G**            **Em**
      Oh, what joy for every girl and boy,
  **C**                      **D**
Knowing they're happy and they're safe.
  **Em**
      We would be so happy, you and me,
  **C**                   **D**
  No-one there to tell us what to do.

*Chorus 3*

  **G**         **Em**
      I'd like to be   under the sea
       **C**     **D**     **Em**
In an octopus's garden with you,
       **C**     **D**     **Em**
In an octopus's garden with you,
       **C**     **D**     **G**
In an octopus's garden with you.

# Paperback Writer

Words & Music by
John Lennon & Paul McCartney

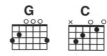

**Intro**

**N.C.**
Paperback writer, paperback writer.

**Link**

| G | G | G | G ‖

**Verse 1**

G
Dear Sir or Madam, will you read my book,

It took me years to write, will you take a look?

It's based on a novel by a man named Lear,

And I need a job,

C
So I want to be a paperback writer,

G
Paperback writer. _____

**Verse 2**

G
It's a dirty story of a dirty man,

And his clinging wife doesn't understand.

His son is working for the *Daily Mail,*

It's a steady job,

C
But he wants to be a paperback writer,

G
Paperback writer. _____

**N.C.**
Paperback writer, paperback writer.

**Link**       | G   | G   | G   | G   ‖

**Verse 3**
             G
It's a thousand pages, give or take a few,

I'll be writing more in a week or two.

I can make it longer if you like the style,

I can change it round,
                        C
And I want to be a paperback writer,
     G
Paperback writer. _____

**Verse 4**
             G
If you really like it, you can have the rights,

It could make a million for you overnight,

If you must return it, you can send it here,

But I need a break,
                     C
And I want to be a paperback writer,
     G
Paperback writer. _____

     N.C.
Paperback writer, paperback writer.

**Link**       | G   | G   | G   | G   ‖

**Coda**     ‖: G
Paperback writer, paperback writer. :‖  *Repeat to fade*

# Rain

Words & Music by
John Lennon & Paul McCartney

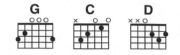

**Intro**　　　|  G　　　|  G　　　|  G　　　|  G　　　||

**Verse 1**

　　　　　　**G**
If the rain comes,
　　　**C**　　　**D**　　　　**G**
They run and hide their heads.
　　　**C**　　　**D**　　　**G**
They might as well be __ dead,
　　　**C**　　　　　　**G**
If the rain comes, if the rain comes.

**Verse 2**

　　　　　　**G**
When the sun shines,
　　　**C**　　**D**　　**G**
They slip into the shade,
　　　**C**　　　**D**　　**G**
And sip their lemonade,
　　　　**C**　　　　　　　**G**
When the sun shines, when the sun shines.

**Chorus 1**

**G**
Rain, _____ I don't mind.

Shine, _____ the weather's fine.

**Verse 3**

　　　　　**G**
I can show you
　　　**C**　　**D**　　**G**
That when it starts to rain,
**C**　　**D**　　　**G**
Everything's the same,
　　　**C**　　　　**G**
I can show you, I can show you.

*Chorus 2*  
**G**  
Rain, _____ I don't mind.

Shine, _____ the weather's fine.

*Verse 4*  
         **G**  
Can you hear me  
**C**       **D**    **G**  
That when it rains and _ shines,  
     **C**  **D**   **G**  
It's just a state of mind?  
       **C**  
Can you hear me?  
       **G**  
Can you hear me?

*Coda*    ‖: **G**   | **G**   | **G**   | **G**  :‖

*Repeat ad lib. to fade*

# Taxman

Words & Music by
George Harrison

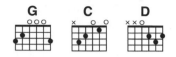

**Intro**      | D     | D     ||

**Verse 1**

           **D**
Let me tell you how it will be:

There's one for you, nineteen for me,
         **C**
'Cause I'm the Taxman,
     **G**       **D**
Yeah, I'm the  Taxman. ____

**Verse 2**

           **D**
Should five percent appear too small,

Be thankful I don't take it all.
         **C**
'Cause I'm the Taxman,
     **G**       **D**
Yeah, I'm the   Taxman. ____

**Bridge**

         **D**
(If you drive a car, car,)  I'll tax the street,
                 **C**
(If you try to sit, sit,) I'll tax your seat,
      **D**
(If you get too cold, cold,) I'll tax the heat,
                 **C**
(If you take a walk, walk,) I'll tax your feet …
**D**
Taxman!

*Solo*      | **D7**    | **D7**    | **D7**    | **D7**    | **D7**    | **D7**    ‖

                     **C**
'Cause I'm the Taxman,

                **G**         **D**
Yeah, I'm the   Taxman.


            **D**
*Verse 3*      Don't ask me what I want it for.

            (A-ah Mister Wilson!)

            If you don't want to pay some more.

            (A-ah Mister Heath!)
                    **C**
'Cause I'm the Taxman,

               **G**        **D**
Yeah, I'm the   Taxman.


            **D**
*Verse 4*      Now my advice for those who die,

            (Taxman!)

            Declare the pennies on your eyes.

            (Taxman!)
                    **C**
'Cause I'm the Taxman,

               **G**        **D**
Yeah, I'm the   Taxman,

                  **F7**
And you're working for no-one but me.


*Solo*      | **D**    | **D**    | **D**    |
           (me.)
           (Taxman!)
           | **D**    | **D**    | **D**    | **D**    ‖ *Fade out*

# Tell Me What You See

Words & Music by
John Lennon & Paul McCartney

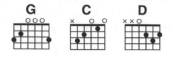

**Intro**  | G  | G  ||

**Verse 1**
G    C     D      G
If you let me take your heart,
       C     G
I will prove to you,
         C     D G
We will never be apart
C     D    G
If I'm part of you.

**Chorus 1**
C        G      C        G
Open up your eyes now, tell me what you see,
C      G     C    D G
It is no surprise now, what you see is me.

**Verse 2**
G    C     D      G
Big and black the clouds may be,
G   C     G
Time will pass away,
       C     D    G
If you put your trust in me,
C     D      G
I'll make bright your day,

**Chorus 2**
C        G      C        G
Look into these eyes now, tell me what you see,
C      G     C    D G
Don't you realise now, what you see is me?

**Bridge 1**
G          C
Tell me what you see.

```
| G     | D     | G     | G     ||
```

**Verse 3**

```
G      C       D          G
Listen to  me  one more time,
            C      G
How can I  get   through?
              C       D        G
Can't you try  to   see that I'm
C          D     G
Trying to get to you?
```

**Chorus 3**

```
C              G          C            G
Open up your eyes now, tell me what you see,
C         G         C      D   G
It is no surprise now, what you see is me.
```

**Bridge 2**

```
G                    C
Tell me what you see.
```

```
| G     | D     | G     | G     ||
```

**Verse 4**

```
G      C       D          G
Listen to me one more time,
              C      G
How can I get through?
               C       D       G
Can't you try  to   see that I'm
C          D     G
Trying to get to you?
```

**Chorus 4**

```
C              G          C            G
Open up your eyes now, tell me what you see,
C         G         C      D   G
It is no surprise now, what you see is me.
G                         C    G
Mmm-mmm-mmm-mmm-mmm.
```

# Thank You Girl

Words & Music by
John Lennon & Paul McCartney

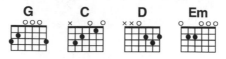

**Intro**   | D     | C     ‖

**Verse 1**
D  C
Oh,   oh,
G      C          G   C
You've ____ been good to me,
               G    D           G   C
You made me glad ____ when I was blue.
G   C     G   C
And ____ eternally, ____
              G   D            G
I'll always be ____ in love with you,

**Chorus 1**
         C          D   C
And all I gotta do is thank you girl,
D
Thank you girl.

**Verse 2**
G  C         G      C
I ____ could tell the world ____
            G   D        G   C
A thing or two ____ about our love.
G  C      G  C
I ____ know little girl, ____
         G   D            G
Only a fool ____ would doubt our love,

**Chorus 2**
         C          D   C
And all I gotta do is thank you girl,
D
Thank you girl.

|          |                   Em           G            D |
| *Bridge* | Thank you girl for loving me the way that you do, |

(Way that you do,)

|          | Em              D              G |
|          | That's the kind of love that is too good to be true, |

|            |       C       D    C |
| *Chorus 3* | And all I gotta do is thank you girl, |
|            | D |
|            | Thank you girl. |

| *Link* | &#124; D      &#124; C        &#124;&#124; |

|           | D   C |
| *Verse 3* | Oh,  oh, |
|           | G      C            G   C |
|           | You've ___ been good to me, |
|           |           G    D         G    C |
|           | You made me glad ___ when I was blue. |
|           | G    C       G    C |
|           | And ___ eternally, ___ |
|           |           G   D           G |
|           | I'll always be ___ in love with you, |

|            |       C       D   C |
| *Chorus 4* | And all I gotta do is thank you girl, |
|            | D |
|            | Thank you girl. |

| *Link* | &#124; D      &#124; C        &#124;&#124; |

|         | D   C   G  C  G  C |
| *Coda*  | Oh,  oh,  oh! |
|         | D   C   G  C  G  C |
|         | Oh,  oh,  oh! |
|         | D   C   G |
|         | Oh,  oh! |

# Twist And Shout

Words & Music by
Bert Russell & Phil Medley

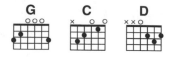

**Intro** | G  C | D   | G  C | D    ||

**Chorus 1**
              **G**        **C**          **D**
Well, shake it up, baby now, (shake it up, baby,)
      **G**       **C**     **D**
Twist and shout, (twist and shout.)
                        **G**        **C**      **D**
C'mon, c'mon, c'mon, c'mon baby now, (come on baby,)
               **G** **C**       **D**
Come on and work it on out, (work it on out.)

**Verse 1**
              **G** **C**        **D**
Well, work it on out, (work it on out,)
               **G**    **C**    **D**
You know you look so good, (look so good.)
               **G**       **C**   **D**
You know you got me goin' now, (got me goin',)
             **G**       **C**      **D**
Just like I knew you would, (like I knew you would.)

**Chorus 2**    As Chorus 1

**Verse 2**
                 **G** **C**     **D**
You know you twist it, little girl, (twist little girl,)
           **G**  **C**     **D**
You know you twist so fine, (twist so fine.)
                **G**       **C**      **D**
Come on and twist a little closer now, (twist a little closer,)
              **G**       **C**     **D**
And let me know that you're mine, (let me know you're mine, ooh.)

*Middle*    | G   C   | D   C   | G   C   | D   C   |

| D   C   | D   C   | G   C   | D   |

(D)
Ah, ah, ah, ah.

*Chorus 3*
                    G           C            D
Well, shake it up, baby now, (shake it up, baby,)
          G        C        D
Twist and shout, (twist and shout.)
                          G           C            D
C'mon, c'mon, c'mon, c'mon baby now, (come on baby,)
                      G  C          D
Come on and work it on out, (work it on out.)

*Verse 3*
                      G  C          D
You know you twist it, little girl, (twist little girl,)
                  G    C       D
You know you twist so fine, (twist so fine.)
                        G          C        D
Come on and twist a little closer now, (twist a little closer,)
                      G          C        D
And let me know that you're mine, (let me know you're mine, ooh.)

*Outro*
                      G          C        D
Well, shake it, shake it, shake it baby now, (shake it up baby,)
                      G          C        D
Well, shake it, shake it, shake it baby now, (shake it up baby,)
                      G          C        D
Well, shake it, shake it, shake it baby now, (shake it up baby,)
D                  G
Ah, ah, ah, ah.

# Yellow Submarine

Words & Music by
John Lennon & Paul McCartney

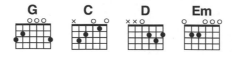

**Verse 1**

D              C   G
In the town where I was born,

Em     C             D
Lived a man who sailed to sea,

G     D     C   G
And he told us of his life,

Em     C           D
In the land of submarines.

**Verse 2**

G     D     C   G
So we sailed up to the sun,

Em     C           D
Till we found the sea of green,

G     D     C   G
And we lived beneath the waves,

Em     C           D
In our yellow submarine.

**Chorus 1**

G              D
We all live in a yellow submarine,

                        G
Yellow submarine, yellow submarine.

                  D
We all live in a yellow submarine,

                        G
Yellow submarine, yellow submarine.

**Verse 3**

(G)    D     C   G
And our friends are all aboard,

Em     C               D
Many more of them live next door,

G     D     C   G     D
And the band begins to play.

*Link*      | G     G | D     G ||

*Chorus 2*

G           D
We all live in a yellow submarine,

                  G
Yellow submarine, yellow submarine.

           D
We all live in a yellow submarine,

                  G
Yellow submarine, yellow submarine.

*Instrumental*  | D    C | G   Em | C      | D    G |

                   | D    C | G   Em | C      | D    G ||

*Verse 4*

(G)   D   C   G
As we live a life of ease,

Em    C             D
Every one of us has all we need,

G   D      C   G
Sky of blue and sea of green,

Em    C         D
In our yellow submarine.

*Chorus 3*

G           D
We all live in a yellow submarine,

                  G
Yellow submarine, yellow submarine.

           D
||: We all live in a yellow submarine,

                  G
Yellow submarine, yellow submarine.  :|| *Repeat to fade*

## Relative Tuning

The guitar can be tuned with the aid of pitch pipes or dedicated electronic guitar tuners which are available through your local music dealer. If you do not have a tuning device, you can use relative tuning. Estimate the pitch of the 6th string as near as possible to E or at least a comfortable pitch (not too high, as you might break other strings in tuning up). Then, while checking the various positions on the diagram, place a finger from your left hand on the:

5th fret of the E or 6th string and **tune the open A** (or 5th string) to the note (A)

5th fret of the A or 5th string and **tune the open D** (or 4th string) to the note (D)

5th fret of the D or 4th string and **tune the open G** (or 3rd string) to the note (G)

4th fret of the G or 3rd string and **tune the open B** (or 2nd string) to the note (B)

5th fret of the B or 2nd string and **tune the open E** (or 1st string) to the note (E)

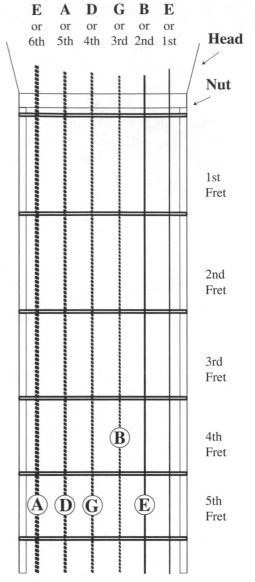

## Reading Chord Boxes

Chord boxes are diagrams of the guitar neck viewed head upwards, face on as illustrated. The top horizontal line is the nut, unless a higher fret number is indicated, the others are the frets.

The vertical lines are the strings, starting from E (or 6th) on the left to E (or 1st) on the right.

The black dots indicate where to place your fingers.

Strings marked with an O are played open, not fretted. Strings marked with an X should not be played.

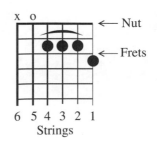

123456789